first field guide
to australian

BIRDS

text: **pat slater**

search &learn

Steve Parish
DISCOVER & LEARN
A B O U T   A U S T R A L I A

Contents

p. 51

BIRDS

p. 19

p. 32

p. 17

p. 44

p. 12

3

Being a birdwatcher

Watching birds is a never-ending adventure and a good way to meet like-minded people. First you can learn to recognise your local birds, then you can travel to new places and add new birds to your lifetime list. You can find out exciting things about even the most common birds. Write down your discoveries and draw, or photograph, the birds' behaviour.

What will I need?

Comfortable clothes and footwear, hat, sunscreen, pair of binoculars, notebook.
A field guide to ALL Australia's 750+ sorts of birds.

How will I begin?

Find a place near birds, then stay still and watch quietly.
In the bush, use your ears as well as your eyes.
In the open, stalk a bird by moving in zig-zags towards it.

Jot down your discoveries in the field, write them up properly at home.

Things to do

- "Birdscape" your garden. Put in a birdbath, feeder, nectar-bearing plants, shelter bushes.
- Build a "hide" at a good birdwatching spot.
- Study one sort of bird in detail.
- Make a list of all the different sorts of birds you see, with dates and places.
- Keep a record of nesting birds, or of migrating[6] birds' arrivals and departures.
- Send your observations to a birders' magazine.
- Go birdwatching with friends.

Home delivery

A bird bath or feeder will bring birds right to your garden, onto your balcony or windowsill. Remember to make your feeder safe from cats.

p. 33

PETER SLATER

How to make a hide

1. Make a wigwam of 3 sticks tied at the top, some distance from bird site.

2. Put bag or canvas around sticks, fasten securely. Gradually move it closer as birds become used to it.

3. Cut peep hole, sit inside. Someone "goes away" then "comes back" to get you out.

Be aware!

⊘ Don't touch nests, eggs or chicks – parent birds may desert them. Watch through binoculars *after* the chicks have hatched.

⊘ Share your discoveries only with people you know will help protect the birds.

⊘ If you are going bush, do so in an adequate vehicle, take water and extra fuel and tell someone your destination.

⊘ Get permission from the owner before entering private property.

⊘ Know that collecting eggs and keeping protected birds without a permit are illegal.

Abbreviations used in this book

m = metres   **cm** = centimetres
g = grams   **kg** = kilograms
♀ = female   ♂ = male
Aust. = mainland Australia
Tas. = Tasmania
Qld = Queensland
WA = Western Australia
NSW = New South Wales
NT = Northern Territory
Vic. = Victoria
G = Glossary (p. 56)

What bird is it?

It's good to go birding with someone else who knows birds, but it's fun to identify new birds for yourself. Soon you will be able to recognise a bird by its "jizz" – you know that only ONE sort of bird looks and behaves like that one.

If you spot a rare bird, get someone else to look at it also to confirm your discovery.

Check these things to identify a bird

Size - more about this on page 7.

Shape - body, neck, bill, legs.

Colour - the parts of a bird are shown below.

Behaviour - what is the bird doing?

Habitatᴳ - where is the bird feeding, nesting etc.

Rangeᴳ - could this bird be in this area?

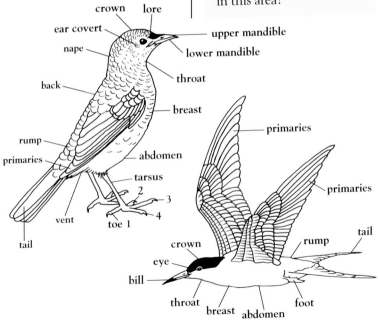

Sizes of some Australian birds

SPLENDID FAIRY-WREN  = EMU

TINY (bill + body length 12–14 cm)	Splendid Fairy-wren
SMALL (19–21 cm)	Willy Wagtail
SMALL–MEDIUM (25–29 cm)	Noisy Miner
MEDIUM (38–44 cm)	Australian Magpie
LARGE (69–76 cm)	White Ibis
VERY LARGE (110–140 cm)	Black Swan
HUGE (height 150–190 cm)	Emu

Date: 4/1/96

Time: 4:30–5:30pm
.Place: Waterhole in State Forest, Moggill, Qld.

Weather: hot, cloudy, no wind

Observers: Sara and Brett Mitchell

Birds seen: Eastern Yellow Robin, Australian King-Parrot, Bar-shouldered Dove, Crested Pigeon, Noisy Miner, Variegated Fairy-wren, Tawny Frogmouth

New bird:
Pale-headed Rosella

white
yellow
pale blue
white
deep blue
sky blue
black
grey
red
sky blue

Notes: Carpet Python 1 metre drank at waterhole. 2 T. Frogmouths in tree near gate.

Bird names

A bird is given:

1. An official common name e.g. Rainbow Bee-eater.

2. A scientific name e.g. *Merops ornatus*. This is written in italics and the word order is reversed from the order in English.

3. Unofficial local names, e.g. "golden swallow", "gold-digger". In Indonesia, this bird's common name is Kirik-kirik-australi, but its scientific name is the same, *Merops ornatus*.

Where to see birds

Because most birds can fly, they often turn up in unlikely places, perhaps driven out of their usual habitat by drought, flood, bushfire, predators or clearing. However, to be sure of seeing a particular bird, you need to go where it can find food, water, safety, a mate and a place to nest.

Many Australian habitats, such as wetlands and heathlands, are very easily damaged or destroyed. Once a piece of habitat disappears, the birds which lived in it die. All other living spaces, or territories[G], are occupied by other birds and the displaced birds simply have nowhere else to go.

If you enjoy watching birds, do your best to protect them and to protect the habitats in which they live.

PETER SLATER

Pale-headed Rosella

When to look for birds

The best time to see birds and to hear them singing is from before dawn to early morning, followed by late afternoon to dusk as a second choice. Fewest birds will be seen in the middle of the day or in rainy or windy weather.

Good places to see birds

Town or city: in parks; on buildings; harbour or riverside; home gardens; road verges; vacant blocks

Bush and open forest: near water; in gullies; on hollow trees; flowering trees; thick bushes

Farmland: near water; irrigation; grain silos; crops; homestead gardens

Rainforest: near water; on leaf litter on forest floor; flowering trees; rainforest edges

Seaside: heathland; dunes; beach; ocean; estuaries; mudflats

Desert: near water; in gullies in ranges; in bushes and trees

Places to study birds more closely: zoo; wildlife park; museum; library

This book contains a selection of Australia's most common and most remarkable birds. There are over 700 more to discover!

Introduced birds: In the past 200 years, a number of birds have been introduced to Australia. They include the House Sparrow, Feral Pigeon, Spotted Dove, Blackbird, Songthrush, Common Starling and Indian Mynah. None appears in this book.

Emu

Dromaius novaehollandiae (= fast-footed Australian)

Pale blue skin on neck and face.

Call: Booming; drumming.

Where found: All over mainland Australia, except for rainforest.

Habits: Lives in small mobs. Eats green plants, seeds and insects.

Nesting: Male incubates[G] 5–15 dark green eggs on ground for about 55 days. Cares for striped chicks for up to 6 months.

Notes: Female larger than male. Inquisitive – wave a handkerchief to bring an emu close. Must drink regularly, so found within range of water. Farmed for leather, meat and oil.

Height: 1.5–1.9 m

Weight: 35–50 kg

Identification: Huge, long-legged, flightless bird. Soft, shaggy grey-brown feathers.

Three island species made extinct by early European settlers.

Status[G]: Common.

Similar species[G]: None.

HABITAT ALL OVER AUSTRALIA

FOOD SEEDS & INSECTS

Southern Cassowary

Casuarius casuarius (= horned head)

Height: 1.5–1.7 m

Weight: ♀ 58 kg; ♂ 34 kg

Identification: Huge, stocky, flightless bird with glossy black feathers. Horny helmet. Bright blue skin on neck and face, red wattles.

Call: Hissing; booming; rumbling.

Where found: Rainforest in northeastern Qld.

Habits: Lives alone. Feeds on fallen fruits.

Nesting: Male incubates 3–4 pea-green eggs on ground for about 55 days. He then cares for the striped chicks.

Notes: Helmet protects head when dashing through forest. Inner toe has long sharp nail and kick can be dangerous.

Status: Threatened as its rainforest habitat disappears. Killed by dogs and vehicles.

Similar species: None.

STANLEY BREEDEN

HABITAT
NE QLD
RAINFOREST

FOOD
FALLEN
FRUITS

Black Swan

Cygnus atratus (= black swan)

Length: 1.1–1.4 m

Wingspan: 1.6–2.0 m

Identification: Very large black swan; white wing-tips, red bill.

Call: Bugling; soft crooning.

Where found: On or near water, anywhere in Australia.

Habits: Usually in flocks. Feeds on water weed and other plants near water.

Nesting: Pair builds nest of reeds and grasses on ground or in shallow water. 4–10 greenish eggs are incubated for up to 45 days. Cygnets stay with parents for 5–6 months.

Notes: Nests after rain. Can fly long distances. Flightless flocks gather on water while moulting⁶. Feed and sometimes breed on city lakes.

Status: Common on wetlands.

Similar species: Mute Swan (introduced species) white, with black face.

 HABITAT NEAR OR ON WATER

 FOOD WATER PLANTS

Little Penguin

Eudyptula minor (= small good-diver)

Length: 40–45 cm

Weight: about 1 kg

Identification: Medium-sized (but smallest penguin). Blue-grey above, white below.

Call: Yaps; grunts; brays.

Where found: In sea off southern coast, or nesting on beach.

Habits: Feeds at sea on fish and other marine animals.

Nesting: Nests on islands or coastal beach, in burrow in sand or under rocks. Two white eggs are brooded by parents in turn for 36 days. Chicks go to sea about 56 days after hatching.

Notes: Only penguin to breed in Australia. Parents come to shore to feed chicks at dusk, go to sea at dawn. Adults moult in burrows. Threatened by oil

spills, habitat disturbance.

Status: Not common. Breeding areas need protection.

Similar species: Rockhopper and Fiordland Penguins are larger and have yellow crests.

HABITAT
SEA &
COAST

FOOD
MARINE
FISH

Australian Pelican

Pelecanus conspicillatus (= spectacled pelican)

Length: 1.6–1.8 m

Wingspan: 2.3–2.5 m

Weight: 4–6.8 kg

Identification: Very large, short-legged, white and black bird with huge pink bill. All four toes webbed.

Call: Soft grunt; groan.

Where found: Anywhere there are water and fish.

Habits: Feeds on fish scooped up in bill and throat pouch. May hunt in large group.

Nesting: Nests on islands. Two eggs laid on ground, brooded by parents in turn for 32–35 days. At 25 days chicks join group "nurseries". They can fly at 3 months.

Notes: Flies high and far in search of fishing grounds. May breed in great numbers on inland lakes after rain.

Status: Common where fish are available.

Similar species: None.

HABITAT
FRESH & SALT WATER

FOOD
FISH

Australian Darter

Anhinga melanogaster (= black-bellied darter)

Length: 86–94 cm

Wingspan: 1.2 m

Weight: 1–2.6 kg

Identification: Large waterbird with thin, kinked neck. Sits upright, often with wings outstretched. Male glossy black; female grey-brown above, whitish below; young very pale.

Call: Rattling clicking; hiss.

Where found: Usually on still, deep fresh water. Sometimes on salt water.

Habits: Spears fish underwater, surfaces to shake them off bill and swallow. Perches with outstretched wings.

Nesting: Large stick nest in tree over water. Male and female both build, then incubate 4 pale green eggs for 28 days. Both feed young, who fledge in about 50 days.

Notes: Swims with only its "snaky" neck and slender head above surface. Sinks without

splash when alarmed.

Status: Common on suitable habitat.

Similar species: 4 species of cormorant, which have shorter, thicker necks and stouter, hooked bills.

HABITAT
DEEP FRESH
WATER

FOOD
FRESH-
WATER FISH

Australasian Grebe

Tachybaptus novaehollandiae (= Australian fast-diver)

RAOUL SLATER

Length: 23–25 cm

Wingspan: 39 cm

Identification: Small, grey-brown waterbird with short bill, short neck, plump body. Yellow patch on head when breeding. Lobed toes. Dives when disturbed.

Call: Trills when courting.

Where found: Freshwater wetlands, farm dams, town lakes.

Habits: Dives for fish, snails, other water animals.

Nesting: Small, round, floating platform of waterweed. Usually 4 eggs, incubated by both parents for 23 days and covered with weed when they leave nest. Chicks stay with parents 8 weeks.

Notes: In pairs or small groups. Stays under water up to 20 seconds. Adults carry chicks on their backs. Grebes eat feathers, to stop fishbones damaging stomachs.

Status: Common in suitable habitat.

Similar species: Hoary-headed Grebe paler, with white streaks on head.

HABITAT
WETLANDS
& LAKES

FOOD
FISH &
WATER LIFE

Silver Gull

Larus novaehollandiae (= Australian gull)

Length: 38–43 cm

Wingspan: 90 cm

Identification: White seabird; adult has grey wings, red legs and beak. Young has brown on back and wings.

Where found: Around southern coasts and on inland waters.

Habits: Gathers in flocks where food is available, near harbours, public beaches, parks. Bold and aggressive.

Nesting: Breeds on offshore islands in dense colonies. Nest is on ground; 2–3 eggs hatch in 21–27 days. Both parents incubate and feed chicks.

Notes: Feeds on fish, scavenges[G] garbage, takes other birds' eggs and chicks. Roosts[G] in large flocks.

Status: Common on southern coasts, some inland waters.

Similar species: Same-size terns have slender wings, black caps, forked tails.

HABITAT
SEA
COASTS

FOOD
FISH; IS A
SCAVENGER

Crested Tern

Sterna bergii (= Bergius's tern)

Length: 46–49 cm

Identification: Medium-sized, white seabird with grey back and wings; short legs; black crown; crested nape; yellow bill. Graceful flier, with slender pointed wings and a forked tail. Dives from some height.

Call: Rasping "krreck".

Range: Australian coasts.

Habits: Dives for fish from 5–15 m above water; rests on sand at high tide with other terns and gulls.

Nesting: Nests in colonies; 1–2 mottled eggs laid in scrape on sand; both parents incubate 25–26 days and care for chicks.

Notes: Commonest Australian tern. Diving terns indicate schools of small surface fish.

Status: Common.

Similar species: Lesser Crested Tern much smaller.

HABITAT
SEA &
COASTS

FOOD
MARINE
FISH

Cattle Egret

Ardea ibis (= heron-ibis)

Length: 48-53 cm

Identification: Medium-sized, stocky, short-necked, white heron. Bill and feet pale yellow. When breeding, has orange-buff neck and back and red bill.

Call: Croaks at nest.

Where found: Wetlands and grazing lands around coastal Australia.

Habits: Usually with cattle or horses, feeding on insects, frogs and other small animals. Roosts in groups over water.

RAOUL SLATER

Nesting: Nests in large colonies with other waterbirds. Male chooses site in tree, attracts female by raising plumes^G, waving nesting sticks. 3-6 pale blue eggs are incubated for 22 - 26 days by both parents.

Notes: Commonly seen with large grazing animals, sometimes on their backs. Probably introduced itself into northern Australia about 1940 and has spread to all States. (It does not breed in Vic. or Tas.)

Status: Common, increasing.

Similar species: Little Egret more slender, with black bill and yellow face.

HABITAT
WETLANDS
PASTURES

FOOD
SMALL
ANIMALS

Black-necked Stork (Jabiru)

Ephippiorhynchus asiaticus (= Asian horse-billed bird)

Height: 1.2 m

Wingspan: 2 m

Identification: Very large, black and white, black-necked wading bird with red legs, strong black bill. Male eye dark, female eye yellow.

Call: Clatters bill.

Where found: Wetlands across northern Australia, south to Sydney, NSW.

Habits: Alone or in a pair, stalking fish, snakes, frogs etc. in shallow water or wet grass. Soars high in air.

Nesting: Nest a huge stick platform in tall tree in swamp. 2–3 white eggs are incubated by both parents.

Notes: Australia's only stork. Pairs for life. Large area of wetland needed to support one pair. Habitat threatened by coastal development.

Status: Disappearing.

Similar species: None.

 **HABITAT** WETLANDS & SWAMPS

 **FOOD** WETLANDS ANIMALS

Brolga

Grus rubicunda (= reddish crane)

Length: ♀ 95–115 cm;
♂ 105–125 cm

Wingspan: 1.7–2.4 m

Identification: Very large, long-legged, pale grey crane with bare red skin on head and grey-green crown. Grey legs.

Call: Trumpeting.

Where found: Wetlands and wet grasslands across northern, western and eastern Australia.

Habits: Small group or large flocks feed on swampland tubers[G] dug up with bills; may eat grain and insects. Wanders widely, may fly at great height.

Nesting: Nest a platform of grass and reeds about 1.5 m across. Both parents incubate 2 white eggs for 28–30 days. Young remain with their parents for up to 1 year.

Notes: Flocks are made up of family groups, each led by a male. Famous for dramatic and graceful "dancing".

Status: Common in north, but disappearing from southeastern Australia.

Similar species: Sarus Crane has pink legs; red skin extends down its upper neck.

HABITAT
WETLANDS
& PLAINS

FOOD
TUBERS &
INSECTS

Australian White Ibis

Threskiornis molucca (= sacred Moluccan bird)

PETER SLATER

Length: 69–76 cm

Identification: Large, white (sometimes dirty), wading bird with naked, black neck and head, long, downcurved bill.

Call: Grunting *urk*.

Where found: Wetlands.

Habits: Moves head from side to side in water while wading, seizing water animals; also takes grasshoppers, small snakes, worms. Probes manure.

Nesting: Builds in flooded swamps. Courting male shows off scarlet patches under wings. Nest a stick platform in reed clump or bush; parent birds incubate 2–5 white eggs in turn for 20–25 days.

Notes: Flock flies in V-formation, all birds flapping then gliding together. When feeding, may hammer mussel shells open with bill. Very adaptable bird, which may scavenge for food in parks, zoos etc.

Status: Common.

Similar species: Straw-necked Ibis has glossy black back. Royal and Yellow-billed Spoonbills have broad, spoon-ended bills.

HABITAT
WETLANDS
& SWAMPS

FOOD
SMALL
ANIMALS

Masked Lapwing

Vanellus miles (= fan-winged soldier)

Length: 33–38 cm

Wingspan: 75–85 cm

Identification: Medium-sized, long-legged wader with grey-brown back, black from forehead down back and sides of neck, white throat and belly. Yellow forehead, mask and wattles. Spur on bend of wing.

Call: Piercing alarm call *keer-kek-kee-kee*.

Where found: Grasslands near water, in northern, eastern and central Australia.

Habits: In pairs or small groups, hunting for insects, other animals and seeds in short grass.

Nesting: Both parents incubate 3–4 blotched eggs in scrape on ground for 28 days. Chicks leave nest soon after hatching.

Notes: Clearing land has provided more habitat and Masked Lapwing may breed in towns. Defends eggs and chicks by diving vigorously.

Status: Common.

Similar species: Banded Lapwing has shorter legs, black "bib", red wattle between eye and bill.

PETER SLATER

HABITAT
GRASSLANDS
& WETLANDS

FOOD
INSECTS
& SEEDS

Purple Swamphen

Porphyrio porphyrio (= purple purple-bird)

Length: 44–48 cm

Wingspan: 70–88 cm

Identification: Large, black-backed, blue or purple-breasted wading bird. Has stout red legs, big feet, and a strong scarlet bill and forehead shield. Flicks tail to show white beneath.

Call: Loud screeching, usually made at night.

Where found: Freshwater wetlands, near reedbeds and nearby pasture, in northern, eastern and southwestern Australia.

Habits: Climbs through reeds, can swim, and runs fast. Rests on roosting platforms. Main diet young reed stems, bitten off then held in foot. Also eats other plants, eggs and small water animals.

Nesting: Group of birds makes a reed platform nest, in which several females may lay. All incubate 3–8 blotched eggs for 23–29 days.

Notes: Lives in pairs or flocks. Sometimes perches in trees. May prey on young water-birds, frogs etc. Becomes tame on parklands.

Status: Common.

Similar species: Dusky Moorhen is black, with slender, yellow-tipped red bill.

HABITAT
WETLANDS
& SWAMPS

FOOD
PLANTS,
ANIMALS

Dusky Moorhen

Gallinula tenebrosa (= dusky small fowl)

Length: 34–38 cm

Wingspan: 55–65 cm

Identification: Medium-sized, black waterbird with white on sides of tail. Has red forehead shield, red bill with yellow tip.

Call: Loud sharp *krek*; squawking.

Where found: Freshwater swamps, lakes with reedy edges and grassy banks.

Habits: A group of 2–7 birds includes a number of males and one female. Often seen swimming, up-ending for water plants. Also graze on banks.

Nesting: Female courts and mates with males in group. All build nest, take turns to incubate 5–8 eggs, then look after young.

Notes: Name comes from "merehen", meaning "bird of the lakes". Reed platforms built for roosting and mating.

Status: Common.

Similar species: Larger Purple Swamphen has a blue breast, a heavy scarlet bill and a scarlet forehead shield.

HABITAT
WETLANDS
& LAKES

FOOD
WATER
PLANTS

Pied Oystercatcher

Haemantopus longirostris (= red-footed long-billed bird)

Length: 48–52 cm

Wingspan: 85–95 cm

Identification: Medium-sized, black and white wading bird with long, scarlet bill and eye-ring, and dull red legs.

Call: Sharp, carrying alarm call *pit-a-peep*.

Where found: Sandy ocean beaches around Australia.

Habits: Alone or in pairs on tideline, pushing bill into sand, feeding on shellfish, worms and crabs. Roosts and rests in flocks.

Nesting: Pair mates for life. Both incubate 2–3 spotted eggs in scrape on sand for 28–32 days. Pretend injury to lead danger from nest or chicks.

Notes: Opens bivalve molluscs by stabbing to cut muscles holding shell or hammering shells until one breaks. Chicks are taught by parents to prise or hammer.

Status: Common.

Similar species: The similarly shaped Sooty Oystercatcher is all-black and usually lives on rocky shores.

 HABITAT
OCEAN
BEACHES

 **FOOD**
MOLLUSCS
& SHORE-LIFE

Comb-crested Jacana

Irediparra gallinula (= Iredale's fowl-like bird)

Length: 20–24 cm
(female larger than male)

Identification: Small to
medium waterbird with
long slender legs and
enormously long toes.
Brown back and wings,
white neck and belly.
Comb on forehead red,
orange or yellow.

Call: Trumpeting alarm;
piping.

Where found: Permanent
freshwater ponds and
lagoons in northern and
eastern Australia, south to
Grafton, NSW.

Habits: Runs over floating
plants, head bobbing, tail
flicking. Eats seeds and shoots
and small water animals.

Nesting: Nest is a frail raft of
plant stems anchored to water
plants. Female courts male,
who incubates 3–4 squiggled
eggs and looks after chicks.

Notes: Also known as "lily-
trotter". Jacanas may escape
danger under water. Adult may
shift eggs or downy young by
carrying them under their
wings, legs dangling.

Status: Common in suitable
habitat.

Similar species: None.

HABITAT
PONDS &
LAGOONS

FOOD
SEEDS &
WATER-LIFE

Australian Bustard

Ardeotis australis (= southern heron-bustard)

Length: ♀ 80 cm; ♂ 1.1–1.2 m

Wingspan: ♀ 1.7 m; ♂ 2.3 m

Identification: Very large, long-legged, plains bird with brown back, white neck and breast. Male has black crown, female has brown crown.

Call: Booming; roaring.

Where found: Grassland, especially in drier northern Australia.

Habits: Feeds during day on plains on grass, seeds, insects such as grasshoppers, and small animals such as mice. When aware of danger it freezes, then walks slowly away.

Nesting: Male displays with throat pouch blown up, wings drooping, head and tail thrown up, strutting and booming. Female incubates 1–2 spotted eggs on ground alone, creeping away if disturbed, then cares for chicks by herself.

Notes: Member of a group becoming rare worldwide. Hunting by humans and foxes, and habitat destruction by sheep and rabbits have reduced numbers greatly. Good flier and may arrive after rainfall.

Status: Disappearing. Needs protection.

Similar species: Bush Stone-curlew is much smaller; it rests during the day and is active at night.

HABITAT
GRASS-
LAND

FOOD
SEEDS &
ANIMALS

Australian Brush-turkey

Alectura lathami (= Latham's cock-tailed bird)

Length: 60–75 cm

Wingspan: 85 cm

Identification: Large, black, strong-legged, ground-living bird with upright, fanlike tail. Grey edges to breast feathers. Naked red head; male wattle larger and bright yellow, female wattle smaller and paler.

Call: Grunting; male booms at nest mound.

Where found: Coastal rainforest, from Cape York south to Gosford, NSW.

Habits: Spends most of the day on the ground. Eats fruit, seed, insects.

Nesting: Male builds nest mound of plant litter and soil. Females visit a mound to lay eggs, then are driven away. Male adds or removes material to keep mound at 33°C . Eggs take about 50 days to hatch, then chicks look after themselves.

Notes: Shy in the forest, but where habitat destruction pushes it into suburbs may become very tame. Mound can take over a garden, but daily care of nest is fascinating to watch. Roosts in trees.

Status: Common, but threatened by habitat destruction.

Similar species: None.

HABITAT
RAINFOREST
& ITS EDGES

FOOD
FRUITS
& SEEDS

Collared Sparrowhawk

Accipiter cirrocephalus (= tawny-headed hawk)

Length: ♀ 36–39 cm; ♂ 28–33cm

Wingspan: ♀ 80 cm; ♂ 55 cm

Identification: Small to medium-sized, long-tailed hawk with rounded wings and square-tipped tail. Grey upperparts, rufous collar, barred rufous and white underparts. Round staring yellow eye.

Call: Repeated shrill *swee-swee-swee*.

Where found: Open woodland and forest, anywhere in Australia.

Habits: Dashes from cover at small birds, mammals, reptiles, seizing victim with long legs; carries prey to perch and plucks it before eating it.

Nesting: Stick nest in a tree fork. Male feeds female while she incubates 2–4 creamy, speckled eggs for 28–30 days. He then supplies food until the chicks are well grown and the female can hunt also.

Notes: Male is our smallest hawk. Fast, agile hunter. Newly fledged[6] young bird has brown back, streaked brown-and-white breast.

Status: Common, but seldom seen.

Similar species: Australian Goshawk is larger, has rounded tailtip and "frowning" brow-ridges.

PETER SLATER

HABITAT WOODLANDS & FORESTS

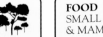

FOOD SMALL BIRDS & MAMMALS

Australian Kestrel

Falco cenchroides (= speckled falcon)

Length: ♀ 35 cm; ♂ 31 cm

Wingspan: ♀ 80 cm; ♂ 60 cm

Identification: Small to medium-sized falcon with long, pointed wings, rufous back, black bar near tailtip, yellow legs. Head of male blue-grey, of female brown streaked with black. Hovers[G] when hunting.

Call: Repeated shrill *ki-ki-ki*.

Where found: Open country, woodland, farms, towns and cities anywhere in Australia.

Habits: Perches or hovers, then pounces on mouse, insect or reptile. Turns up at insect and mouse plagues.

Nesting: Uses other birds' stick nests, tree hollows, cliffs or ledges of high buildings. 3–7 pale buff blotched eggs are incubated for 28 days by the female, who is fed by the male.

Notes: Female is larger than male. Lives anywhere prey and nest places exist. Harmless to

PETER SLATER

poultry. A farmer's friend.

Status: Common.

Similar species: Brown Falcon is larger, with longer, blue legs, scruffier appearance.

HABITAT FARMLANDS & OPEN SPACES

FOOD MICE & INSECTS

31

🦅 Wedge-tailed Eagle

Aquila audax (= bold eagle)

Length: ♀ 1.0 m; ♂ 90 cm

Wingspan: ♀ 2.3 m; ♂ 1.85 m

Identification: Very large eagle; young bird has gold-brown head and back, adult is black. Legs feathered to toes. Often soars, showing fingered wings and wedge tail.

Call: Double whistle *pee-yaa*.

Where found: Open country and open forest, hills and ranges throughout Australia; seldom near human dwellings.

Habits: Soars on rising air currents, spotting carrion such as road kills; also takes live prey, especially rabbits.

Nesting: Male courts female with aerial displays⁶. Huge stick nests built in tall tree; female incubates 1–3 buff splotched eggs; male feeds her and later feeds chicks.

Notes: Australia's largest bird of prey. Persecuted in the past, now one of the Outback's prized sights. All-dark plumage at 6–7 years.

Status: Common in suitable habitat.

Similar species: None.

HABITAT
PLAINS &
OPEN FOREST

FOOD
ANIMALS
& CARRION

Crested Pigeon

Ocyphaps lophotes (= swift pigeon with a crest)

Length: 30–34 cm

Identification: Medium-sized grey pigeon with crest on head, coloured speculum^G on each black-barred wing, pink legs. Takes off with loud whistling of wings, then alternately flaps and glides.

Call: Cooing; sharp *wook*.

Where found: Dry grasslands near water on mainland Australia, avoiding dense forests. Common around farms.

Habits: Gathers in flocks to feed on ground on seed and at water.

Nesting: Nests after rainfall. Courting male bows and spreads wings and tail; in display flight, rises steeply up, then glides down again. Nest a frail stick platform in bush or tree; both parents incubate 2 white eggs for 18–20 days. Feed chicks "pigeon milk", then seed.

Notes: Has increased its range with human agriculture.

Status: Common.

Similar species: The 2 other crested pigeons have different habitats, Topknot in rainforest, Spinifex in central desert.

RAOUL SLATER

HABITAT
GRASSLAND
NEAR WATER

FOOD
GRAINS
& SEEDS

Wonga Pigeon

Leucosarca melanoleuca (= white-meated, black and white bird)

Habits: Alone or in pairs, feeding on seeds and fruit on forest floor. Flushes with loud clap of wings.

Nesting: Courting male stands on ground or log, swinging tail up and down, tucking head behind each spread wing in turn, showing off boldly marked breast. Nest a platform of twigs in tree, vine or fern. 2 white eggs are incubated 17–18 days.

Length: 38–40 cm

Identification: Medium-sized, plump, ground-living pigeon with grey upperparts, white face, white V mark on breast, white belly speckled black. Bill is red, tip brown; feet are pink.

Call: Loud *coo* repeated twice a second up to 100 times.

Where found: Dense coastal forests, from Rockhampton, Qld to Melbourne, Vic.

Notes: Has disappeared as habitat destroyed. Once prized for eating, because its flesh remains white when cooked.

Status: Common in suitable habitat.

Similar species: Only forest-dwelling pigeon with broad white V on breast.

 **HABITAT** COASTAL FORESTS

FOOD FRUITS & SEEDS

Sulphur-crested Cockatoo

Cacatua galerita (= cockatoo with a crest)

Length: 45–50 cm

Identification: Medium to large white cockatoo with long, narrow, yellow crest, which is raised and fanned in excitement. Strong grey-black bill.

Call: Harsh screeching.

Where found: Forests and open country in northern and eastern Australia.

Habits: Gathers in large flocks when not breeding; feeds on seeds, bulbs, roots, insect larvae on ground in cooler part of day. When sitting around, may strip bark and leaves from trees.

Nesting: Nests in tree hollow, usually near water, sometimes in cliff holes. 2–3 white eggs incubated 30 days.

Notes: These cockatoos are sociable and endlessly active; it is sad to see one in a small cage. To nest, they need large old trees with big hollows.

Status: Common.

Similar species: Corellas have pale bills, lack yellow crest.

HABITAT
WOODLANDS
& FORESTS

FOOD
SEEDS
& BULBS

Rainbow Lorikeet

Trichoglossus haematodus (= hair-tongued blood-red bird)

Length: 30–32 cm

Identification: Medium-sized lorikeet with red bill, blue head, brilliant green upperparts, red-gold breastband and blue belly.

Call: Metallic screech.

Where found: Coastal lowlands of northern and eastern Australia, especially on flowering trees. Perth, WA.

Habits: Swift-flying, noisy flocks search for flowering trees. Birds feed with tongues tipped with "hairs", which mop up nectar. Also eat fruit, seeds, insects. Roost in camps, chattering and screeching before settling to sleep.

Nesting: Pairs for life. Nest in tree hollow; female incubates 2 white eggs 28 days, fed by male. Both parents feed young.

Notes: Introduced to Perth, WA, and now breeds there. Comes to garden feeders, even in large towns.

Status: Common.

Similar species: Scaly-breasted Lorikeet flocks with Rainbow, but has "scaly" green and gold breast.

HABITAT
FORESTS &
SUBURBS

FOOD
NECTAR
& SEEDS

Crimson Rosella

Platycercus elegans (= flat-tailed, elegant bird)

Length: 32–36 cm

Identification: Medium-sized parrot with red head, rump, and underparts; back is mottled red and black. Cheek patches, outer wing feathers and tail are blue. In eastern SA, some birds have yellow replacing red.

Call: Screeching; bell-like chiming; chattering.

Where found: Edges of forest and woodland in eastern and southeastern coastal Australia, from Cairns, Qld, to SA.

Habits: Flocks wander forest edges looking for seeds and fruit, feeding in trees and on ground. Young ones roam more widely than mated adult pairs.

Nesting: Pair for life. Courting bird spreads and wags tail (see Pale-headed Rosella p. 8). Female incubates 4–5 white eggs in tree hollow for 19–21 days; both parents feed chicks.

Notes: May become very tame around camp grounds and picnic spots.

Status: Common.

Similar species: King-Parrot is larger and has green back.

HABITAT
WOODLANDS
& FORESTS

FOOD
FRUITS
& SEEDS

🐦 Shining Bronze-Cuckoo

Chrysococcyx lucidus (= shining golden-cuckoo)

Length: 17–18 cm

Identification: Small, plump bird with loose-looking feathers, fine bill. Shining green-bronze back, striped underparts. Flies in up-and-down pattern on slender, pointed wings.

Call: Male calls in repeated high, rising whistle, like someone calling a dog.

Where found: High rainfall coastal areas from Cape York, Qld to SA, and the southwest of WA.

Habits: Winters north of Australia, arrives in Australia August, breeds by January, then most migrate north again. Eats insects, including hairy caterpillars, which most birds will not touch.

Nesting: Male attracts female by calling. After mating, female places egg in nest of host; cuckoo hatches in 17 days, shoves out hosts' eggs or chicks, then is raised by hosts. A female may lay up to 16 eggs a season.

Notes: Hosts usually small birds with domed nests, e.g. fairy-wrens.

Status: Common, but only calling male easy to spot, after following call.

Similar species: Horsfield's Bronze-Cuckoo has dark spot on cheek, is paler in colour.

GRAEME CHAPMAN

HABITAT WOODLANDS & FORESTS

FOOD CATERPILLARS, OTHER INSECTS

Pheasant Coucal

Centropus phasianinus (= spur-footed pheasant-like bird)

Length: 50–60 cm

Identification: Large, long-tailed, loose-feathered, ground-living bird which suns itself in treetop at dawn, scuttles without warning across road. In breeding season, has glossy black head, back, breast, wings barred russet, buff, black. Non-breeding head and back buff and russet.

Call: Repeated bubbling *oop-oop-oop*, first falling, then rising and getting faster.

Where found: Dense undergrowth and grasses in coastal northern and eastern Australia.

Habits: Hunts insects, frogs, mice and other small animals.

Nesting: Nest of leafy twigs and grass on platform trampled in a bush. Both parents incubate 2–5 white eggs for 15 days, then feed young. May nest again while young still being fed in area.

Notes: Sometimes wrongly thought to be a pheasant. Bubbling call betrays birds hunting in outer suburban gardens at dawn. Young will leave nest early if disturbed.

Status: Common where suitable habitat exists.

Similar species: None.

RAOUL SLATER

HABITAT
WOODLANDS
& GRASSES

FOOD
SMALL
ANIMALS

Barn Owl

Tyto alba (= white owl)

Length: 30–40 cm

Identification: Medium-sized, pale-coloured owl, with heart-shaped white facial disc around dark eyes, pale bill and long, bare legs. White underparts, grey-gold upperparts; wings are spotted black and white.

Call: Rasping hiss, like cloth ripping.

Where found: All over Australia, especially open woodland and plains.

Habits: Favourite food mice, so often seen around farm buildings. Hunts after dark, watching from perch then pouncing silently. Builds up numbers in mouse plagues, but many owls die afterwards.

Nesting: Breeds when food is plentiful. Nests in tree hollow or cave. Female incubates 3–7 white eggs for 33–35 days; male helps feed chicks.

Notes: Locates prey by sound and has keen night vision. Roosts during day in hollow, foliage or cave. Under roost are pellets of food remains.

Status: Common in suitable habitat, but seldom seen.

Similar species: Grass Owl (a rare inhabitant of grasslands) has tawny-brown back. Masked Owl is larger.

HABITAT ALL OVER AUSTRALIA

FOOD SMALL ANIMALS

Southern Boobook

Ninox novaeseelandiae (= New Zealand night-bird)

Length: 25–35 cm

Identification: Small, dark-coloured owl with a circular disc around each yellow-green eye, dark bill and shortish, feathered legs. Upperparts brown with white spots, underparts streaked white, wings barred.

Call: Repeated *boo-book*, second note lower.

Where found: All over Australia.

Habits: Hunts for small roosting birds, insects and small mammals in hours after sunset and before sunrise.

Nesting: Courting pair sits side by side preening[G] each other. Nests in tree hollow. Female incubates 2–4 white eggs for about 30 days while fed by male; both parents feed young.

Notes: Other birds will mob roosting Boobook, which sits upright, feathers sleeked. May live in suburbs, catch moths at outdoor lights, visit bird baths.

Status: Common.

Similar species: Barking Owl larger, white blotches on upperparts, bold white streaks on underparts. Barking call.

IAN MORRIS

HABITAT ALL OVER AUSTRALIA

FOOD SMALL ANIMALS

Tawny Frogmouth

Podargus strigoides (= trap-footed owl-like bird)

Length: 35–53 cm

Identification: Medium-sized night-bird, whose mottled and streaked grey, brown, black and white feathers and upright posture camouflage[G] it as broken-off branch. Wide bill, weak legs, small feet.

Call: Soft, repeated, far-carrying *oom-oom-oom.*

Where found: All over Australia.

Habits: Often seen in a pair, or family group. Roosts during day, freezing and sky-pointing bill if disturbed. Hunts after dark, perching then flying down to snap up insects, frogs and other small animals with wide, sharp-edged bill.

Nesting: Male and female mate for life. They build a flimsy stick nest in a tree fork, incubate 1–3 white eggs for 28–32 days, then both feed the young.

Notes: Garden insecticides eaten with prey may be stored in body fat. When fat is used in cold weather, poisons cause convulsions, death.

Status: Common.

Similar species: Marbled and Papuan Frogmouths are seldom-seen rainforest species.

PETER SLATER

HABITAT
ANYWHERE
WITH TREES

FOOD
SMALL
ANIMALS

42

Sacred Kingfisher

Todirhamphus sancta (= sacred tody-bill*)

Length: 19–23 cm

Identification: Small kingfisher with black mask, buff spot in front of eye, white collar, blue-green upperparts, blue edge to wings, blue tail; pale buff underparts.

Call: Repeated *kik-kik-kik*.

Where found: All over Australia, except for driest parts, in spring and summer. Spends period March to October in islands to the north of Australia.

Habits: Usually alone, sitting on wire or branch, watching for insects, frogs or reptiles. May catch tadpoles, small fish in shallow water.

RAOUL SLATER

Nesting: Pair digs tunnel in termite nest, tree limb or earth bank. Take turns to incubate 3–6 white eggs for 16–17 days, then both feed chicks.

Notes: May be killed by cats when pouncing on ground prey in gardens.

Status: Common.

Similar species: Forest Kingfisher has white patch in wing; Red-backed Kingfisher has head streaked white.

* Todies are West Indian birds.

HABITAT
ANYWHERE
EXCEPT DESERT

FOOD
SMALL
ANIMALS

43

Laughing Kookaburra

Dacelo novaeguineae (= New Guinea kingfisher)

Length: 40–45 cm

Identification: Medium-sized kingfisher with dark mask, dark eye, brown upperparts, white collar and underparts. Pale blue on wing, brown tail is barred black. In flight, shows white band across wing.

Call: Chuckling; loud "laughing" made by group to claim territory.

Where found: Woodland and open forest in northeastern, eastern and southeastern Australia; introduced to southwestern WA.

Habits: Alone or in pairs, sitting on wire or branch, watching for insects, frogs, reptiles. Prey battered on perch, then swallowed.

Nesting: In a tree hollow or hole in termite mound. 1–4 white eggs incubated for 24 days by female and helpers, who also feed chicks.

Notes: Unmated young birds, up to 4 years of age, help their parents raise new chicks.

Status: Common.

Similar species: Blue-winged Kookaburra, across northern Australia, has white, streaked head, pale eye, more blue on wing. Shrieking call.

 HABITAT
WOODLANDS
& FORESTS

 FOOD
SMALL
ANIMALS

Rainbow Bee-eater

Merops ornatus (= ornate bee-eater)

Length: 21–24 cm

Identification:
Dainty, slender-winged, green-gold bird with fine down-curving bill, black mask, black throat, gold on head and under wings, two long central tail feathers.

Call: Repeated *prrrp-prrrp*, often in flight.

Where found: Open country with trees and bushes to perch on, soil or earth banks for nesting, anywhere in Australia except Tas.

Habits: Usually with other bee-eaters, sitting on wires or branches, darting out to take dragonflies, wasps or other insects on wing.

Nesting: Nest in 1 m tunnel dug into flat, sandy ground or earth bank. Mated pair may be helped by young, unmated birds. 4–5 white eggs are incubated for 21–25 days. Young leave nest at 1 month.

RAOUL SLATER

Notes: Breeds in Australia, most spend winter in islands to Australia's north. Sometimes roosts in large groups.

Status: Common in summer.

Similar species: Kingfishers have straight, stout bills.

HABITAT
OPEN
COUNTRY

FOOD
FLYING
INSECTS

Superb Lyrebird

Menura novaehollandiae (= mighty-tailed Australian bird)

Length: ♂ 80–100 cm (of which tail is 50–60 cm)

Identification: Large, brown ground-bird. Male has long filmy tail, thrown over back when he displays; female has shorter, plainer tail.

Call: Male is master of song and mimicry.

Where found: Coastal wet forests of southeastern Australia; introduced to Tas.

Habits: Scratches forest floor for small animals. Male claims territory by singing and dancing on earthen display mounds; females come to the mound to mate.

Nesting: Female builds a domed nest of sticks, incubates 1 blotched egg for up to 50 days, then cares for young.

Notes: Depends on wet forest habitat for survival.

Status: May be endangered.

Similar species: Albert's Lyrebird, smaller and with shorter tail, in northeastern NSW and southeastern Qld.

HABITAT
WET
FORESTS

FOOD
FOREST
FLOOR ANIMALS

Splendid Fairy-wren

Malurus splendens (= shining soft-tailed bird)

Length: 12–14 cm

Identification: Tiny, plump bird with long, cocked tail. Adult male pale blue crown, cheek patches and upper back, black mask and collar; back black and blue, wings and underparts blue. Female and young male are brown.

Call: Trilling *treee*; loud, rich, warbling song.

Where found: Open forest and woodland in central and southwestern Aust.

Habits: Family group consists of pair plus helpers, usually young males from past broods. Feeds on insects and other small creatures.

Nesting: Female builds domed nest of grass and bark in bush, incubates 3–4 spotted eggs for first part of 13–15 days. Helpers aid later incubation, then assist in feeding chicks.

Notes: High mortality from cats and fire, in spite of good

PETER SLATER

family care of chicks. Intruder male may invade territory carrying a flower, then be accepted by a female as mate.

Status: Common.

Similar species: Superb Fairy-wren in southeastern Australia has black back and breast, white underparts.

HABITAT
OPEN
WOODLANDS

FOOD
SMALL
LIFE

Spotted Pardalote

Pardalotus punctatus (= spotted spotted-bird)

RAOUL SLATER

Length: 90–100 mm

Identification: Tiny, short-tailed, stubby-beaked bird which feeds in treetops. Black crown, wings and tail, spotted with white; yellow to red back and rump, yellow undertail. Female paler than male.

Call: High *sleep-baby*.

Where found: Wetter forests in eastern, southeastern and southwestern Australia.

Habits: Moves fast through leaves of eucalypts feeding on lerps and other insects. Out of breeding season feeds in flocks, which may move to warmer feeding grounds in winter.

Nesting: A pair digs a nest tunnel in an earth bank, wall, or mound of garden soil. In a nest chamber lined with bark and grass, they take turns to incubate 3–6 white eggs for 14 days, then feed the chicks.

Notes: Pardalotes are only found in Australia and make their living in the crowns of eucalypts. The Forty-spotted Pardalote, found only in southeastern Tasmania, is an endangered species.

Status: Common.

Similar species: Striated Pardalote is found all over Australia. It has white streaks on its head, but no spots.

HABITAT
EUCALYPT
FORESTS

FOOD
TREETOP
INSECTS

Noisy Miner

Manorina melanocephala (= black-headed thin-nose)

Length: 25–29 cm

Identification: Small, loud-voiced, aggressive honeyeater common in gardens. Grey upperparts, white underparts, black face. Yellow bill, bare skin behind eye and legs.

Call: Loud scolding *zwit*; in flight calls *teu-teu-teu*.

Where found: Woodlands in eastern and southeastern Australia. A common and obvious garden bird.

Habits: Lives in groups consisting of up to 30 birds, which defend territory by shrieking and mobbing. May drive same-size birds of all types away. Feeds on nectar, fruit, insects.

Nesting: Nest is a cup of bark and grass in the outer foliage of a tree. Dominant[G] female of the group builds nest, lays 3–4 speckled eggs.

Group members incubate eggs for 15–16 days, feed chicks.

Notes: Miners signal each other with calls, by posing and by raising or lowering head feathers to hide or show the yellow skin near their eyes.

Status: Common.

Similar species: The Yellow-throated Miner is found west of Great Dividing Range; it lives in smaller groups.

RAOUL SLATER

HABITAT
WOODLANDS
& GARDENS

FOOD
INSECTS
& NECTAR

Eastern Yellow Robin

Eopsaltria australis (= southern dawn-harper)

Length: 14–15 cm

Identification: Small, plump bird with grey upperparts, yellow rump, white chin, yellow underparts. White wingbar shows in flight.

Call: Loud whistle *tewp-tewp* before dawn; soft piping.

Where found: Forests and woodlands with bushy undergrowth, in eastern Australia.

Habits: Alone, in pairs, or in small parties, sometimes with other small birds. Hunts insects by perching, watching, then pouncing. May cling sideways to tree trunk.

Nesting: Mated pair holds territory. Female builds cup nest of bark and grass bound by cobwebs, decorates outside with lichens, in tree fork. Male feeds her while she incubates 2–3 spotted eggs for 15–16 days. Both parents, plus helpers from previous broods, feed young.

Notes: A quiet and charming bird, which may become tame in a garden, or around a picnic place.

Status: Common.

Similar species: Western Yellow Robin in southwestern WA.

RAOUL SLATER

HABITAT
WOODLANDS
& FORESTS

FOOD
INSECTS &
SMALL LIFE

Golden Whistler

Pachycephala pectoralis (= breasted thick-head)

Length: 16–17 cm

Identification: Small, large-headed bird which sits upright, moves slowly when feeding. Male has black head and collar, white throat, golden nape and breast, green upperparts. Female is grey-brown, with white throat.

Call: Rich *wh-wh-wh-you wit*, with whipcrack ending.

Where found: Forests of southern and eastern Australia and southwestern WA.

GRAEME CHAPMAN

Habits: Alone or in pairs, hops through trees, flies around foliage, eating insects.

Nesting: Male and female both sing, defend territory, build a cup nest of plant stems, leaves held together with cobweb in a fork. Take turns to incubate 2 spotted eggs for 14–17 days. Both feed young.

Notes: A loud noise may start whistlers singing their beautiful, rich notes. In winter, mountain and southern birds may move to warmer areas.

Status: Common.

Similar species: Mangrove Golden Whistler only in northern mangroves. Rufous Whistler has red-brown breast.

HABITAT
WOODLANDS
& FORESTS

FOOD
INSECTS &
SMALL LIFE

Willy Wagtail

Rhipidura leucophrys (= white-browed fan-tail)

Length: 19–21 cm

Identification: Small bird with black upperparts and throat, white underparts and eyebrow. Long tail is fanned and wagged from side to side.

Call: Rattling in aggression; song *sweet-pretty-creature* often given on moonlight night.

Where found: Anywhere on mainland and northern Tas. Farms, suburbs.

Habits: Perches, then flies to catch insects; hops around taking prey on open ground.

Nesting: May nest near human dwelling. Male and female build cup of bark and grass, stuck together with cobwebs, on branch. Both incubate 2–4 spotted eggs for 14 days, then feed the chicks.

Notes: Willy Wagtail shows dominance by flashing white eyebrow. Uses sheep, cattle as perches. Noisy and aggressive towards hawks, snakes, cats.

Status: Common.

Similar species: Restless Flycatcher has a white throat makes scissor-grinding call, hovers over grass looking for insects.

RAOUL SLATER

HABITAT SUBURBS & FARMLANDS

FOOD INSECTS

Australian Magpie

Gymnorhina tibicen (= flute-playing naked-nose)

Length: 38–44 cm

Identification: Medium-sized, strong-legged bird with black head and underparts, white nape, white on wing. Both sexes have black backs over most of eastern and northern Australia; male has white back, female ashy-grey back in Vic., Tas., southwest of WA.

Call: Loud, sweet song; softer whisper-song includes mimicry of other birds.

Where found: Open country with trees, all over Australia. Farms, suburbs, cities.

Habits: A group of up to 24 birds defends territory, feeds on ground on insects and other small animals. Dominant male mates with several females.

Nesting: Neighbouring groups battle with song for territory. A female build a nest of sticks in a tall tree, lays 3–5 blotched eggs, incubates 20 days and feeds young. Once out of the nest, young may be fed by others in group.

Notes: Nests supported by dominant male have best chance of succeeding. Young are later driven from group and form roving flocks. (If magpies defending nests become aggressive, wear a hat, or take another route.)

Status: Common.

Similar species: None.

HABITAT
SUBURBS &
FARMLANDS

FOOD
INSECTS,
SMALL LIFE

Satin Bowerbird

Ptilinorhynchus violaceus (= blue feather-bill)

RAOUL SLATER

Length: 27–33 cm

Identification: Medium-sized blue-black bird with mauve eyes (male), or with green upperparts, creamy underparts marked with spots on throat, scallops on breast and belly (female and young male).

Call: Near bower, male chatters, buzzes, creaks, and mimics other birds and sounds.

Where found: Mountain and coastal forests in eastern Australia, from Atherton Tableland, Qld, to Otway Ranges, Vic.

Habits: Flocks in autumn and winter, seeking fruit and seeds. In spring, males return to their bowers, which are avenues of sticks built in forest clearings. They decorate these with blue objects, then dance and sing to attract females.

Nesting: Female mates with male with finest bower, then builds saucer of twigs in tree, incubates 1–3 spotted and blotched eggs for 21–22 days, then raises young by herself.

Notes: Males do not get full blue plumage until they are 6 or 7 years old. Until then they practise bower-building. Bower may be painted with plant juice, charcoal, saliva.

Status: Common in suitable habitat.

Similar species: None.

HABITAT
COASTAL
RAINFORESTS

FOOD
FRUITS &
SEEDS

Zebra Finch

Taeniopygia guttata (= spotted banded-rump)

Length: 10 cm

Identification: Tiny red-billed finch with black and white on face, grey upperparts, chestnut cheek patches, black and white rump, white spots on red flanks.

Call: Nasal *tang*.

Where found: All over Australia except Cape York Peninsula, extreme southwest and southeastern Tas.

Habits: Found where there is grass seed to eat, bushes to nest in, water to drink. Can survive dry conditions. Lives in flocks, roosts in special grass nests.

Nesting: Breeds whenever rain has fallen and seed is plentiful. Nest is a woven ball of grass with a side tunnel entrance. The male fetches grass, while the female builds. Both birds incubate the 4–5 white eggs for 12–14 days, then both feed the young.

Notes: One of the world's best-known cage birds, with white and other colour varieties.

Status: Common.

Similar species: None.

RAOUL SLATER

HABITAT
GRASS-
LANDS

FOOD
GRASS
SEEDS

Glossary ^G

camouflage. Colouring, markings or outline which hides a bird in a particular place.

displays. Behaviours which birds use to communicate with other birds. Involve song, movements, plumage.

dominant. First in importance.

fledged. A young bird's feathers have grown and it is ready to leave the nest.

habitat. A place which supplies a bird's needs for food, breeding and protection from enemies.

hovers. Remains airborne without moving forward.

incubates. Keeps eggs at a constant temperature until they hatch.

migrating. Moving from one place to another as seasons change etc.

moulting. Yearly process of shedding feathers and growing new ones.

plumes. Ornamental feathers used in courtship and other displays.

preening. Putting feathers in order. May include waterproofing them with oil from preen gland on rump.

range. Area in which a particular bird is normally found.

roosts. Settles down to sleep.

scavenge. To eat food not killed but found dead or otherwise available.

species. A group of animals whose members can breed with each other and produce fertile offspring.

status. How many of a species exist and whether numbers are increasing or decreasing.

speculum. Patch of coloured feathers on the wing of a duck or a pigeon.

territories. Areas claimed by pairs or groups of birds as feeding and breeding grounds.

tubers. Underground stems.

Recommended further reading

LINDSAY, T.R. 1992. *Encyclopedia of Australian Animals: Birds*. Angus & Robertson, Sydney.

MORCOMBE, M. 2000. *Field Guide to Australian Birds*. Steve Parish Publishing, Brisbane.

READER'S DIGEST. 1982. *Reader's Digest Complete Book of Australian Birds*. Sydney.

SLATER, P. 2000. *Encyclopedia of Australian Wildlife*. Steve Parish Publishing, Brisbane.

SLATER, P., P., R. 1989. *Field Guide to Australian Birds*. Lansdowne, Sydney.

SLATER, P., PARISH, S. 1997. *Amazing Facts About Australian Birds*. Steve Parish Publishing, Brisbane.

PHOTOGRAPHY: Steve Parish (uncredited) and Australia's finest bird photographers Raoul Slater, Peter Slater, Graeme Chapman, Stanley Breeden, Ian Morris, as credited.
ACKNOWLEDGEMENTS: The author's thanks are due to Peter Slater and to Allan Fox for their helpful comments on the text, and to Leanne Nobilio whose talent for design has contributed so much to this series. Audra Colless designed the cover and title page.

First published in Australia by Steve Parish Publishing Pty Ltd
PO Box 1058, Archerfield, Queensland 4108 Australia
www.steveparish.com.au
© copyright Steve Parish Publishing Pty Ltd, 1997
ISBN 1 74021 054 9